THIS JOURNAL BELONGS TO

INTRODUCTION

KUAN YIN is the beautiful sacred rebel of the East. A bodhisattva of the Tibetan tradition, she loves all of humanity and reaches out to offer healing, guidance, compassion and unconditional divine love to help every heart become free from fear and open to love. True spiritual masters offer unconditional love. This means they do not judge or deny you based on your history or your religious choices. They simply reach out to you to bring peace, comfort and encouragement on your life path.

One of the most beautiful demonstrations of the unconditionality of divine love comes through in a story shared by a Frenchman who was travelling in China. He became separated from his tour group at the onset of a dangerous snow storm. He didn't know what to do and in a moment of fear, he prayed to his beloved Mother Mary for her intervention. In the sky, he saw a petite Asian woman in what he thought were long silk pyjamas, pointing in a particular direction. He followed her guiding hand and soon found a cave in which to rest and be protected from the storm overnight.

The next morning, he arose to find the storm had passed and he was safe to venture out and search for his group. When he looked at the cave in the light of day, he was stunned to see how exposed it was. It looked far too open to have been the comfortable haven he had been so grateful for during the storm. He spotted a village within walking distance and to his delight, he found his tour group there. He also found paintings of the woman he had seen in the sky after his prayers. He asked who she was and the villagers told him it was Kuan Yin.

There's much to love about this story. There is the practice of faith and the miraculous appearance of a comfortable shelter that later appeared to be inadequate for the task it had performed. And then, there is the demonstration of how the Divine Mother expresses her compassion through a 'network' of holy ones to bring aid in the best and quickest way possible for all those that seek help – regardless of what their culture, beliefs or traditions may be.

You don't have to be in dire straits to call on the Divine Mother in any of her unconditionally loving expressions such as Kuan Yin. She will help you in the smallest moments of indecision and with the greatest choices or challenges you face on your life journey. She does this because the Divine loves you and wants to help you to successfully navigate and create your life journey so as you may experience all the blessings meant for you.

You can write to Kuan Yin in this journal, you can connect with her using one of the oracle decks I have created in her honour (*Kuan Yin Oracle* and *Wild Kuan Yin Oracle*) and you can reach out to her in prayer. You can also use the mantra, "Om Mani Padme Hum." This mantra or ancient spoken prayer empowers us to open our souls to an unconditionally loving and generous spiritual grace. Pronounce this mantra as, "om man-ee pad-may hum." However, the intention you speak the mantra with is more important than your pronunciation. Getting the words to sound right is helpful, but not essential for the prayer to work its divine love in your life.

Kuan Yin is now reaching out to you. She has heard your heart. She brings you comfort and a message to trust that she is already working with you to bring healing and grace into your world.

One of her most empowering messages is to let go of striving and forcing, and simply trust your intention is powerful enough to set your Universe in motion! Your heart-felt prayer and desire is enough. Allow yourself to be moved, inspired, and trust that the Universe knows what it's doing. Do what you can in whatever situation you find yourself in. Don't fight or resist it. Be graceful and surrender into it. No matter what it looks like, you are being led to your higher destiny and you don't have to worry about the details. The Divine Mother, Kuan Yin, is an intuitive, attentive and intelligent spiritual tour guide, helping you avoid pitfalls and hidden traps, and directing you along the most beautiful scenic route. In true Kuan Yin style, this also happens to be the most efficient and effective way to manifest your heart's desire.

When you trust in the Universe – and the Divine Mother – in this way, you are allowing a great and benevolent creative power to amplify what is in your heart, to attract what you need and to show you possibilities even more beautiful than what you can currently imagine.

Kuan Yin was always breaking rules and getting into trouble during her lifetime. She shows us that sometimes you must break free and be true, even if it means taking risks. The chances that she took led her to some dark places, but through those experiences, she learned how to love more. She also had the opportunity to practise her particular spiritual power: radical forgiveness. In doing so she became completely free from karma and thus experienced spiritual illumination and absolute freedom. She loves humanity so much that she chose to stay connected to the earth to help all in need until there is no more suffering on the planet. This is the depth of this great spiritual master's devotion, love and compassion.

Kuan Yin helps us learn about the true power of forgiveness in very practical, everyday situations. She is the queen of divine forgiveness. Whenever we forgive ourselves and others in a way that stretches and surprises us, we are becoming more free, more empowered and a more potent channel of divine love. We feel increased peace and happiness. True forgiveness is not about letting someone get away with something – not ever. It's a divine affirmation. It says:

This poison is less important to me, less real, than the truth of divine love. That's the place I want to dwell. That's the place that means something real to me. That's what I choose for myself. And my ticket there is forgiveness. So, I give that to myself – and to you. It's up to you to choose it, but that's what I'm choosing.

You can feel how this expression of the Divine Mother is gentle, kind and peaceful, and also incredibly strong. She can shift even the darkest pain through her unwavering compassion and unconditional love. For everyone that wants to change the world through a healed heart, who understands that the Divine doesn't seek to dominate us but wants us to use our free will to choose joy and love, Kuan Yin is a guide, a sacred sister and a dear friend who helps us strengthen our loving connection to the great beloved in our own hearts.

May you realise Kuan Yin's blessings are upon you. May her grace reach you through these words and take you to a place of comforting reassurance. May you trust that all is working out perfectly, that your heart's wishes are known, coming into being and will manifest in divine perfection. Your struggle has not been in vain. It is now time to soften and allow yourself to be helped, blessed and lifted into a more beautiful experience of life. Let us finish this introduction with her mantra. This special prayer is said more than any mantra in the world. Om Mani Padme Hum.

May you dwell in the divine beauty of your heart,

– Alana

Kuan Yin Oracle and *Wild Kuan Yin Oracle* by Alana Fairchild are available through Blue Angel Publishing. You can learn more about Kuan Yin in Alana's book *Crystal Masters 333 - Initiation through the Divine Power of Heaven and Earth*, and also in the beautiful *Crystal Mandala Oracle*. Visit Alana online at **www.alanafairchild.com**

YOU HAVE THE POWER TO CO-CREATE YOUR BEAUTIFUL LIFE BY OPENING
TO THE LOVE THAT THE DIVINE MOTHER HAS FOR YOU.

YOUR SOUL LIGHT CAN RADIATE AND UPLIFT OTHERS, REMINDING THEM
OF THE WAY OF LOVE RATHER THAN FEAR.

YOU ARE READY TO GROW THROUGH THE UNFAMILIAR,
TO BELIEVE IN YOURSELF AND TO TRUST IN LOVE.

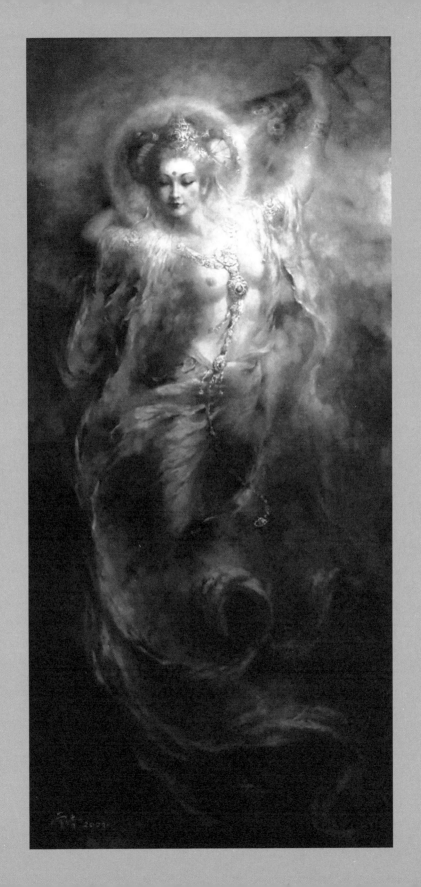

SPEAK YOUR TRUTH. IT SHALL SET YOUR SOUL FREE.

THERE ARE NO MISTAKES IN THE UNIVERSE. ALL EVENTS,
CIRCUMSTANCES, RELATIONSHIPS AND SITUATIONS ARE UNFOLDING
PERFECTLY TO NURTURE YOU INTO FULLNESS.

RELAX AND TRUST IN THE UNFOLDING OF YOUR DIVINE DESTINY.

Ask this of yourself today, "May I have compassion for myself in the same way I do for others. May I accept and meet my needs for wellness and fulfilment. May I receive healing with grace and gratitude."

THE UNIVERSE SEEKS TO REPLENISH, RESTORE
AND CREATE THROUGH YOU.

ALLOW YOURSELF TO RECEIVE BEYOND WHAT YOU HAVE THOUGHT
POSSIBLE BY OPENING YOUR HEART WITH GRATITUDE NOW.

OUR HEARTS NEED TO BE OPEN ENOUGH TO RECEIVE THE MAGNIFICENCE
OF THE BLESSINGS OFFERED TO US. OTHERWISE, IT IS LIKE ASKING AN
OCEAN TO BE CONTAINED IN A THIMBLE!

THERE IS NO NEED FOR SPIRITUAL SHAME OR FEELINGS OF INADEQUACY.
NO MATTER WHAT HAS HAPPENED IN YOUR LIFE, WHAT YOU HAVE
EXPERIENCED OR THE CHOICES YOU HAVE MADE, YOUR SOUL LIGHT IS AS
PURE AS THE DIVINE SOURCE ITSELF. ESSENTIALLY, THAT IS WHAT IT IS!

EVEN THE HEAVIEST HEART AND MOST BURDENED MIND BECOMES LIGHT,
FREE AND JOYFUL IN THE PRESENCE OF THE DIVINE.

YOU DON'T NEED TO FORCE THINGS TO HAPPEN.
TRUST, LET GO, ALLOW YOUR CREATIVITY TO FLOW.

A prayer, "Please help me, beloved Kuan Yin, so that my creation may manifest swiftly and gracefully, with beauty and perfection."

REJOICE: "MAY I KNOW AND LIVE ALL OF MYSELF, MAY MY LIFE
BE FILLED WITH LIGHT, ENERGY AND WARMTH, LIKE SPRINGTIME
AFTER THE WINTER."

DEEP WITHIN, YOU KNOW.

Oh, the joy of letting it go!

YOU CANNOT BE A PIONEER OF NEW CONSCIOUSNESS ON THIS PLANET
IF YOU FEEL COMPLETELY COMFORTABLE IN THE CONSCIOUSNESS THAT
ALREADY EXISTS AROUND YOU. NOT 'FITTING IN' IS PART OF WHAT
EMPOWERS YOU WITH A DIFFERENT VIEWPOINT AND A FREER, MORE
FEARLESS AND LOVING VOICE.

YOU ARE CALLED TO RISE AGAIN AND AGAIN, TO LIVE UP TO YOUR
POTENTIAL, WITH ALL ITS UNIQUENESS AND BEAUTY.

曾浩

Zeng Hao 2001

A DIVINE BLESSING IS ON ITS WAY TO YOU.

PROMISE YOURSELF, "I GIVE MYSELF PERMISSION TO MAKE CHOICES
THAT HONOUR MY TRUTH, MY HEART, MY SOUL."

FORGIVENESS OF SELF AND OTHERS HELPS YOU DISCONNECT YOUR
ENERGETIC CIRCUITS FROM PEOPLE, PLACES, SITUATIONS AND
MEMORIES THAT CAN DRAIN YOUR POWER FROM THE PRESENT MOMENT,
SLOW DOWN YOUR SPIRITUAL GROWTH AND IMPEDE THE PHYSICAL
MANIFESTATION OF YOUR HEART'S DESIRE AND SOUL PURPOSE.

GRACE IS THE INTERVENTION OF COMPASSIONATE, UNCONDITIONALLY LOVING, DIVINE INTELLIGENCE THAT HELPS YOU REALISE YOU HAVE LEARNED ALL YOU CAN. IT IS NOW TIME FOR YOU TO BE ASSISTED OUT OF A SITUATION – TO BE LIFTED UP.

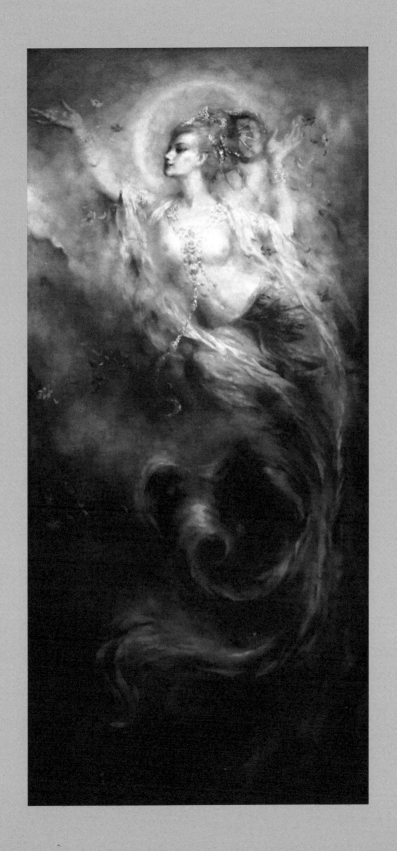

KUAN YIN URGES YOU TO LET THE HEAVINESS OF THE PAST GO.
ALLOW YOUR HEART TO BECOME AS LIGHT AS AIR, AS IF IT HAS GROWN
WINGS AND CAN FLY.

YOU DO NOT HAVE TO BE PERFECT TO DESERVE LOVE AND FORGIVENESS,
YOU JUST NEED TO BE WILLING TO RECEIVE IT.

PROCLAIM: "I NOW CHOOSE TO SURRENDER STRUGGLE AND DOUBT, AND
OPEN TO THE BLESSINGS OF KUAN YIN'S DIVINE GRACE THROUGH WHICH
ALL MANNER OF THINGS BECOME POSSIBLE."

JUST LIKE THE PHOENIX THAT IS BAPTISED THROUGH CELESTIAL FIRE
TO BE BORN ANEW, YOU ARE GOING THROUGH A PHASE OF HEAVENLY
PURIFICATION, PREPARATION AND INITIATION.

WHEN WE PREPARE TO MOVE HOUSE, WE SORT THROUGH OUR POSSESSIONS
AND LET GO OF ANYTHING WE DO NOT WISH TO TAKE INTO OUR NEW LIFE.
WHEN WE PREPARE TO MOVE TO A HIGHER LEVEL OF CONSCIOUSNESS, OLD
HABITS, STUCK EMOTIONS AND STAGNANT ENERGIES THAT DO NOT BELONG
IN OUR NEW LIFE MUST LIKEWISE BE SURRENDERED.

DO NOT FEAR THE CHALLENGES. YOU WOULD NOT BE TAKING
THESE 'SPIRITUAL EXAMS' IF YOU WERE NOT READY.
HAVE FAITH IN YOUR PROGRESS.

LETTING GO OF OLD ENERGIES WITH TRUST – EVEN WHEN YOU DO NOT
CONSCIOUSLY UNDERSTAND WHAT IS HAPPENING – IS THE QUICKEST WAY
TO ASCEND EASILY AND GRACEFULLY.

THERE IS NOTHING TO BE GAINED BY MAKING LIFE MORE DIFFICULT
THAN IT NEEDS TO BE. ALLOW THE DIVINE MOTHER TO HELP YOU NOW.
TRUST THAT YOU DESERVE TO BE NOURISHED AND ASSISTED ON
YOUR PATH.

DECLARE: "WITH TRUST AND PEACE, I NOW RELEASE ANY ENERGY, CORD OR ATTACHMENT THAT NO LONGER SERVES MY SOUL'S ASCENSION. I CALL UPON KUAN YIN, THE BELOVED DAUGHTER OF THE PHOENIX AND HEAVENLY FIRE, TO BLESS AND ASSIST ME NOW."

Enlightenment is made manifest through the small actions
we take each day. Sometimes the smallest action can feel like
an enormous leap, and yet when that action is taken, we realise
the journey into peace is something we can choose to take
at any moment.

ZengHao 曾浩
2000.

YOUR SPIRITUAL LEGACY ON THIS PLANET IS IMPORTANT. YOU ARE
HELPING LOVE TO GROW FOR FUTURE GENERATIONS.

WHEN YOU ASK THE DIVINE FOR ANSWERS, THEY WILL COME MORE
EASILY WHEN YOU DON'T OVERTHINK. RELAX AND AT THE RIGHT TIME,
YOU SHALL JUST KNOW.

PRONOUNCE: "DIVINE MOTHER, GUIDE ME. RESTORE ME. I TRUST YOU
COMPLETELY. YOUR WISDOM, LOVE AND JOY LIGHTS MY PATH AND THE
WAY BECOMES EASY FOR ME."

IF WHAT YOU ARE THINKING OR FEELING IS FEARFUL, DON'T BELIEVE IT.
THERE IS ALWAYS A MORE LOVING TRUTH TO BE FOUND.

DO NOT GIVE IN TO SOCIAL CONDITIONING THAT TELLS YOU TO
COMPROMISE YOUR VALUES, YOUR BELIEFS OR YOUR COMPASSION IN THE
PURSUIT OF SUCCESS.

Any struggles you have experienced are a karmic gift to help you grow your inner light. You are becoming strong, peaceful and radiant in a world that needs your light.

JUST LIKE A BEAUTIFUL AND RARE NATURAL PEARL, YOU HAVE A UNIQUE
SPIRITUAL BEAUTY TO OFFER TO THE WORLD.

AFFIRM OUT LOUD: "I USE ANYTHING THAT CAUSES ME DISCOMFORT TO GROW MY LIGHT SO IT BECOMES BIGGER THAN THE DISCOMFORT AND MY HEART AND MIND RETURN TO PEACE."

Connect through prayer, "I now call for the peaceful resolution of any situation or struggle that I am involved in, consciously or unconsciously, through the divine grace of the beloved priestess in the Temple of Jade, Ma Kuan Yin."

YOU ARE A POWERFUL BEING OF LIGHT. EVEN WHILE YOU ARE IN
FLOW WITH UNIVERSAL FORCES, YOUR STRONG ROOTS HELP YOU TO BE
AT PEACE WITH YOUR TRUTH, AND TO STAND YOUR GROUND WHILE
YOUR LIGHT SHINES TRUE.

YOU ARE STRONGER THAN YOU REALISE.
BE BRAVE AND STAY TRUE TO YOURSELF, BELOVED.

If you want to give a roar, do it! Stick your tongue out and make a sound as you free the divine power within.

TAKE CARE OF YOURSELF. AN EMPTY CUP CANNOT FILL ANOTHER.